*"There are a hundred ways to
kneel and kiss the ground."*
—-Rumi

"Look deep into nature, then you will understand everything."
—-Einstein

*"Every part of this earth is sacred to my people. Every shining pine needle,
every sandy shore, every mist in the dark woods, every clearing and humming
insect is holy in the memory and experience of my people."*
—-Chief Seattle

Acknowledgements

"One finger cannot lift a pebble."—Hopi proverb

"It takes a thousand voices to tell a single story."—Native American proverb

A book is never the solitary work of a writer. One always stands on the shoulders of all who taught, encouraged, and cheered the writer on. Many associates worked on this story and added to its energy namely, David W. Craig, illustrator, Streetlight Graphics Designers, Kristin Nitz, editor, and Linda McLean. Ripples and Waves stands on the incredible story of the Mother Earth Water Walkers and their determined leader—Josephine Mandamin.

To all—Chi Miigwetch.

Ripples and Waves

Copyright © 2019 by Carol Trembath

Paperback ISBN: 978-0-9907446-6-5

Library of Congress Control Number: 2017901217

Illustrations by David W. Craig

Lakeside Publishing MI

Printed in the United States of America

RIPPLES
AND
Waves

Written by Carol Trembath
Illustrated by David W. Craig

Dedication Page

THIS BOOK IS DEDICATED TO Grandmother Josephine Mandamin, an Anishinaabe (Ojibway) member and founder of the Mother Earth Water Walkers.

Many years ago Josephine saw that our precious water was in trouble. Water was being polluted and siphoned away. She took up the challenge given to her by the Grand Chief of the Three Fires Midewiwin Lodge when he asked, "What are you going to do about it?"

With the Great Lakes at the heart of the historical Anishinaabe territory, Josephine decided to draw attention to the condition of water by walking the perimeter of each of the Great Lakes. In the spring of 2003, Josephine and a group of supporters began their first water walk by circling Lake Superior. Since then water from lakes, rivers, and even oceans has been carried in copper pails over countless roads in an effort to show others the importance of protecting the water.

Today Josephine's message continues to send out ripples and waves to communities across the Midwest and beyond. There is an ever widening circle of concerned citizens and civic leaders who are exploring a new vision for water—one that ensures a sustainable future for all of Earth's living inhabitants.

With every step there has been a growing certainty within Josephine regarding her mission, but she felt some concern over my endeavor to write children's books about the Water Walkers story. She shared her uneasiness when she wrote to me, saying:

"I have had misgivings about what you are doing. Many offerings have been made for an answer to my misgivings. In our culture we tell oral teachings or draw. In your culture, it is different. To that I give my respect. I have pondered on the reason why you are doing this. I pondered about ego, money, fame. What is it she wants, I asked? Finally, the response came:

'It is for the water. Simple—for the water. I give my blessings for the water. Now I can rest easy."

Both Josephine's real life story and Little Mai's adventure with her grandmother in this book, *Ripples and Waves*, speak to the heart and soul of this nation. We are all one and part of the Great Circle. Josephine is moving forward to build a deeper awareness of water and of the impact of American culture on the environment.

When asked why she is doing this, she replied, "We are not doing this for ourselves, we're doing this for you. What will you tell your grandchildren when they ask, *What did you do for the water?*"

About the Water Walkers

THE MOTHER EARTH WATER WALKERS began their journey in 2003 when Native women walked 1,372 miles around Lake Superior. In 2004, 2005, 2006, and 2007 the Mother Earth Water Walkers encircled Lake Michigan, Huron, Ontario and Erie respectfully. In 2008 the Water Walkers revisited Lake Michigan. In 2009 Lake Ontario was circled from Kingston, Ontario to the Atlantic Ocean along the St. Lawrence River.

In 2011 Native people walked from four directions: from the Atlantic, Pacific, Hudson Bay, and the Gulf of Mexico and came together to pour the healing waters of the oceans into Lake Superior. Beyond the Great Lakes, the Mother Earth Water Walkers walked down rivers including the Mississippi River in 2013 and the Ohio River in 2014. In 2015 the Mother Earth Water Walkers walked from Quebec, Canada to Madeline Island. In 2017 they walked from Duluth, Wisconsin to Quebec. For the past fourteen years they have walked over 19,000 miles to call attention to the sacred gift of water.

The Ojibway (or Chippewa), Ottawa (or Odawa), and Potawatomi are known as the "Council of Three Fires." According to Native tradition, the Ojibway were the caretakers of the Eastern Woodlands and Great Lakes. The Anishinabek women as givers-of-life were responsible for speaking for, protecting, and carrying the water. Their walk with a copper pail of water was a way of *walking the talk*. Walking, the slowest form on transportation, reinforced an ancient value of taking a public stand. Each of the steps was a prayer for the water, Mother Earth, animals, birds, insects, trees, and the human family.

Lake Huron was the location of the third water walk in 2005 which began at Sault Ste. Marie, Ontario. Lake Huron is named for the Wyandot people, and Huron Nation who lived there. It was the first of the Great Lakes to be explored by the French explorers. They called it La Mer Douce, meaning fresh-water sea.

A few years after Columbus landed in the new world, Native people began migrating westward away from the eastern side of North America. This migration took 300-400 years. Tribes spread out across the Great Lakes area and many connections among the indigenous people were lost. One intention of the Ojibway's third water walk, was to connect with the chiefs and other First Nation people around Lake Huron. Native people have recognized that this is the time of the Seventh Fire—a time of coming together in strong communities to help the planet and one another.

The story *Ripples and Waves* is a reminder of Native people's ongoing endurance and task of protecting Mother Earth. The following is a children's fiction story. It is a tribute to the Native women and men who have walked countless miles to draw attention to the condition of water. It is an "imaginary version" that describes what many dedicated and courageous indigenous people have done to protect and preserve water for generations to come. If you would like to learn more about the Mother Earth Water Walkers, go to their website at motherearthwaterwalk.com.

My mother looked up from her spinning and said, "Mai, your grandmother is preparing for the Ojibway's third water walk. I remember everything you told me about your water walks around Gitchi-gami and Michi-gami. I like spinning yarn into thread; you like spinning words into stories."

"Can I go on another water walk and bring back more stories?" I asked. "Please?"

"Why don't you go outside and ask your grandmother? She said you are a good water walker."

8

I grabbed my coat and ran to our campfire circle. I saw my grandmother with other Ojibway members. I asked her, "Can I go with you on the next water walk?"

"Yes, Mai, you can go. I want to connect with other First Nation tribes around Lake Huron and raise awareness about the harm being done to the Great Lakes. Many of the relationships with Native people around Lake Huron have been lost or broken, but water connects us all.

"We are sending out ripples and waves of friendship along the Great Lakes. Our message is not for just indigenous people. We will watch and see how far these blue ripples go."

Soon my grandmother, my sister Winona, my Uncle Joe, and many other Ojibway members gathered in the city of Sault St. Marie, Michigan. After a departing ceremony, we crossed into Canada. Grandmother said, "In about two weeks, we will cross back into Michigan at the Blue Water Bridge in Sarnia, Ontario. Then we will follow Lake Huron's shoreline up to the Mackinac Bridge on our way back to Sault St. Marie."

Birds and people watched us traveling with our copper pail and eagle staff. We saw pine tree forests. I touched their soft needles and smelled their green scent. The trees became our friends to protect us from the cold winds of early May. Grandmother said, "Trees are the lungs of the earth. They give us fresh air."

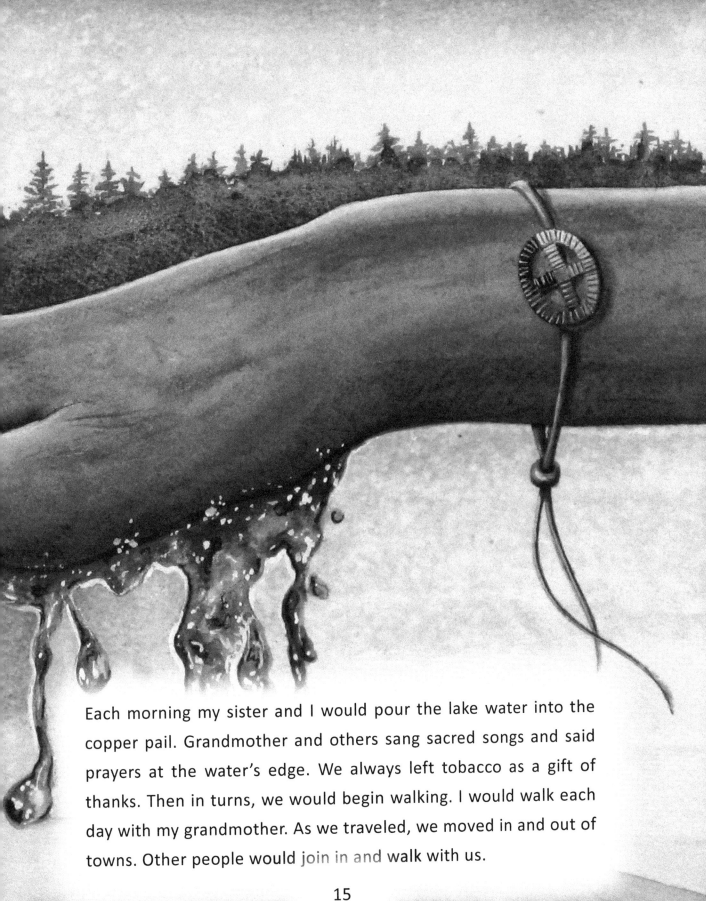

Each morning my sister and I would pour the lake water into the copper pail. Grandmother and others sang sacred songs and said prayers at the water's edge. We always left tobacco as a gift of thanks. Then in turns, we would begin walking. I would walk each day with my grandmother. As we traveled, we moved in and out of towns. Other people would join in and walk with us.

16

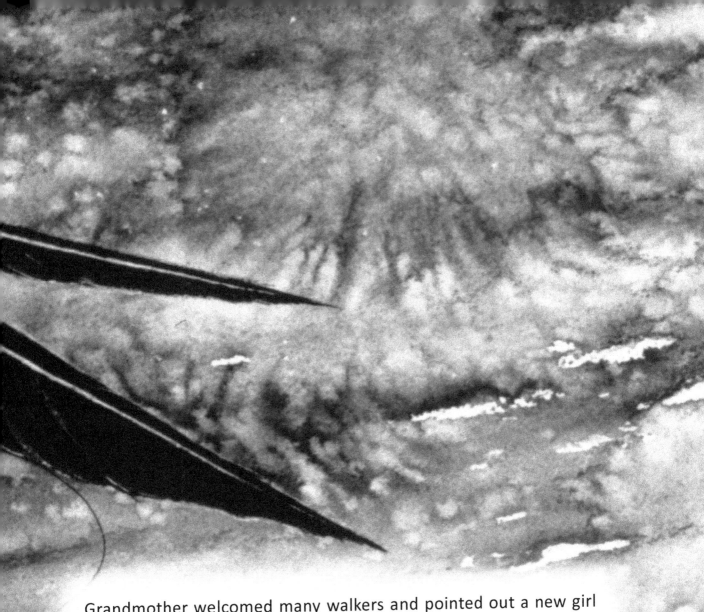

Grandmother welcomed many walkers and pointed out a new girl who was my age to walk with. Her name was Kaiya. Kaiya and I told each other many stories. Together we decided to look for cans and bottles to recycle.

Before long Kaiya said, "Why don't we make dreamcatchers and give them to boys and girls at the Eastern Doorway? It might be a way to make new friends. I brought some things along with me to make them."

"Oh, yes," I said. "That sounds like fun. I used to watch my Uncle Joe make snowshoes and weave a web just like we do when we make dreamcatchers.

"My grandmother told me that Spider Woman was the spiritual protector of our tribe. But when the Ojibway people began to grow

18

and spread across the land, Spider Woman couldn't continue to watch over all of us. That is why she created the first dreamcatcher and gave it to the Ojibway. I had a dreamcatcher by my cradleboard, did you?"

"Yes, me too."

20

As Kaiya and I traveled along the shores of Lake Huron, we both looked for feathers, stones, and shells on beaches to add to our dreamcatchers. Kaiya said, "I am going to add four beads to my dreamcatcher: a red, yellow, black, and white—to represent each color of the four directions of the Medicine Wheel."

I said, "I am going to add to my dreamcatcher four features of Mother Earth: a sea shell for water, a pretty stone for earth, a feather for air, and a piece of red cloth used to make prayer ties for fire. Our dreamcatchers look different, but it's all right---because it is okay to be different. We like being friends, and we can be different too."

24

When we reached the Eastern Doorway, Grandmother was greeted by many Anishinabek tribes including meeting the mighty Shawanaga First Nation. Their chief agreed to walk with us. Kaiya and I began to talk with the Shawanaga children.

As our greeting gift, we brought our dreamcatchers. Near the Shawanaga Reserve, I asked a young girl, "Would you like to have one of our dreamcatchers?" But she shied away from us, saying, "No."

We were surprised. We thought *our* dreamcatchers might catch more dreams of clear, blue water and friendship.

I asked Winona what was wrong. She said, "Sometimes it takes time to make new friends and build their trust. There are differences even among First Nation tribes.

"We are now in the time of the Seventh Fire, and it is about making connections and coming together as community. The earth is our home. Her creeks, streams, and rivers flow into our lakes and oceans. Water connects us."

Grandmother was listening and added, "You can learn much from Mother Earth where all things are connected. She has many stories to tell and different ways of looking at things. In nature there is no judgement about whether a tree is good or bad. It is about *diversity*.

"We are all in the lodge of the Creator. Our common kinship is Mother Earth and her blue water. Today we are tying knots of friendship and weaving threads of community together."

Another Shawanaga chief spoke. "Many chiefs, natives, and non-natives, have agreed to walk together to honor the water. We see what has been left behind in our shared history. We are now stepping forward together.

"Mai and Kaiya, go again and talk with our children. Like your dreamcatcher's web, there are no straight lines in nature. Life presents many turns in the road and it is sometimes hard to walk in new shoes. Build friendships and honor the water."

Kaiya and I held hands and we said, "We will tie more knots of friendship too. We will walk for the water and make many more ripples and waves. *We know we can.*"

Make a Dreamcatcher

NATIVE PEOPLE CONSIDER DREAMS TO be very important. The Ojibway were the first among many tribes in North America to create dreamcatchers. It is a craft that has become popular only in the last 100 years. There are no artifacts of dreamcatchers in museums and ancient burial sites. In addition, they are not part of the traditional and important seven ancient teachings.

However, Native people often reflect those beliefs when making a dreamcatcher or an art piece. A Native person will many times give away their first creation as a gift. It is a way of demonstrating the idea of love and generosity. Another teaching that is considered in the making of dreamcatchers, is by deliberately putting a flaw somewhere in the design to show humility. This mirrors the idea that only the Creator can make something perfect.

Also, dreamcatchers speak about dreams that are either good or bad. However, Native teachings emphasize nature as being *neutral and diverse*.

The dreamcatcher legend says that good dreams go through the hole in the center reaching the sleeper, but the bad dreams are caught in the webbing and dissolve in the morning sun. Dreamcatchers are usually hung where a person sleeps. When a baby is born, a dreamcatcher is often hung on the child's cradleboard. Over time special mementoes such as a feather, shell, or photo, are often added to the dreamcatcher.

Dreamcatchers are traditionally made from willow tree branches, sinew, feathers, and beads. The willow branch is soaked in water to make it bend into a circle without breaking. The ends are then tied together. However many non-traditional items can be purchased at a conventional craft store. Young students may need help from a grown-up when creating their first dreamcatcher.

What You Will Need To Make Your Own Dreamcatcher:

- Scissors, ruler, and all-purpose crafts glue.
- A macramé ring 3", 6" in diameter
- Suede lace (2 yards) and sinew (leather or synthetic string) (3 yards).
- A clip to hold suede in place after gluing.
- Beads you can string on the suede lace and several feathers.

What to do:

1. Cut a five foot piece of suede leather. Tie one end to the circular frame.

2. Wrap the lace around the frame to cover it, pulling it tight as you go. Cut off any extra lace. Glue, then hold the lace end in place with a clip while the glue sets.

3. Cut a 1 yard piece of sinew. With one end, make a half-knot at the top of the circle.

4. In a clockwise motion, make half knots (half-hitch) across the circle, about an inch apart. Continue clockwise, keep using half-knots to make the rest of the web.

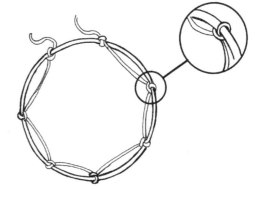

5. Gently tighten each half-knot in the center of your circle to make the middle hole of the web. Tie off the web with two knots. Cut off any extra sinew.

6. String beads as you go along. Knot one end so the bead will not fall off.

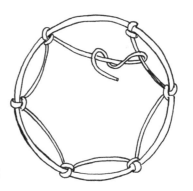

7. Tie feathers to the web with remaining sinew.

8. Hang the dreamcatcher over your bed. Sweet dreams.

Words to Know

Anishinaabe – Indigenous people also named First Nations or aboriginal; many of whom live in U.S. states in Michigan, Wisconsin, and Minnesota, and in Canada in the provinces of Quebec, Ontario, Manitoba, and Saskatchewan.

Biodegradable – Materials that can be broken down by natural processes and absorbed harmlessly into the environment.

Climate change – A measurable change in the Earth's climate, temperature, and weather patterns that scientists believe to be the result of global warming.

Conservation – The protection of animals, plants, and natural resources.

Council of Three Fires – A long-standing Anishinabek alliance of the Ojibway (or Chippewa), Ottawa (or Odawa), and Potawatomi tribes of North America.

Cradleboard – A wood frame worn on the back of Native women for carrying an infant.

Dreamcatcher – A circular framed net with a hole in the center that is used by some Native people to help block bad dreams and catch the good dreams.

Eagle Staff – The eagle staff is a highly honored and sacred object. It commonly looks like a shepherd's staff and is wrapped in either otter or buffalo skin. It displays eagle feathers. In Native traditions it is said that eagles communicate with Creator. The eagle staff, in turn, becomes a conduit for prayer.

Eastern Doorway – A metaphor for the general easterly direction and location on the back of the "Great Turtle" (North America).

Elder – An older person who is respected for their knowledge and experience.

Environment – The conditions that surrounds someone or something that affects its growth, health, and/or progress; the natural world around us.

First Nations – One of the groups of people whose ancestors lived in North America before the arrival of the Europeans.

Four Directions – The Native people see the world as having four directions. From the four directions, North, South, East, West, come the four winds. Each direction has a special meaning and color associated with it.

Global warming – An increase of the average temperature of the Earth's atmosphere that many scientists consider to be the cause of adverse effects such as climate change, melting polar ice caps, decreasing air quality, and rising sea levels.

Greenhouse effect – The process by which gases that accumulate high in the Earth's atmosphere trap heat from the sun, hold it, and bounce it back to Earth. This causes a warming effect upon the Earth's surface, oceans, and atmosphere.

Indigenous – Existing, growing, or produced naturally in a particular region or environment.

Medicine Wheel – A metaphor for a variety of spiritual concepts. A stone circle built by Native people believed to have religious, territorial, and/or calendar significance.

Midewiwin – A society created by Native people to share and protect the songs, ceremonies, and sacred teachings of and for the Anishinabek people.

Prayer Ties – A traditional sacred bundle of tobacco that are instilled with a person's wishes, prayers, intentions, and especially messages of "thank you".

Recycling – The process of reusing materials that would otherwise be thrown away. Recycling saves energy, helps conserve the world's forests, and reduces waste.

Seventh Fire – An Anishinaabe prophecy that marks phases or periods in the life of the people on Turtle Island (a Native name for North America).

Three sisters – The three main agricultural crops of various Native groups in North America: winter squash, maize (corn), and climbing beans.

Turtle Island – The Anishinabek name for the North American continent.

Water cycle – The continuous, natural process by which water evaporates from bodies of water, collects in the atmosphere as vapor, condenses in clouds, falls to the ground as rain, and evaporates again.

Water pollution – The addition of harmful substances such as fertilizers, pesticides, sewage, oil, or toxic waste to natural water.

10 Things You Can Do
To Protect the Earth

Save Earth's Natural Resources

The Problem: The human population is growing fast and so are people's demands on the Earth to help us live. The Earth can only reproduce these things so quickly. We need to conserve our natural resources so we do not run out of water, food, and fuel.

1. Save Water. Turn off the faucet while brushing your teeth and you can save up to 1-1½ gallons of water. Taking a shower uses much less energy than filling a bathtub. A shower uses 10-25 gallons of water, while a bathtub uses up to 36 gallons. Even washing your hands and turning off the water as you soap-up, then turning it back on to rinse, is a great way to save water.

2. Save Electricity. Turn off the lights when you leave a room. Remind grown-ups to unplug small equipment like battery chargers for phones and video equipment. They use energy even when they are not plugged into anything. Replace burned-out light bulbs with energy-saving low wattage bulbs. At night, turn off computers.

3. Save Fuel. Heating our homes in the winter and cooling them in the summer, takes lots of energy. Ask parents to raise (in the summer) and lower (in the winter) the thermostat a few degrees. It will save energy and money.

Stop Using Plastic!

Problem: Plastic wraps, containers, and water bottles are polluting our land and water. 90% of plastic bottles are not recycled!

4. Reuse Water Bottles. Fill them with regular tap water.

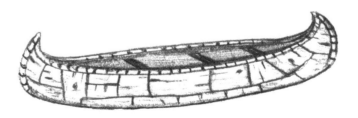

Reduce, Reuse, Recycle!

The Problem: The human population is increasing and so is the amount of things we use and throw away. Earth can't keep up with all of our garbage. We have to start thinking of ways to reduce, reuse, and recycle.

5. Recycle. Talk to your parents about organizing your family trash. Help your family get into the habit of recycling paper, newspapers, cardboard, plastic bottles, cans, aluminum, and glass containers. Make four labels: Aluminum, Paper, Plastic, and Glass. Tape one sign on each of four home, trash containers. Start or participate in a school recycling program too!

6. Reuse. A huge amount of paper and plastic is wasted on shopping bags. Ask parents to buy a few cloth bags that you can always use for shopping.

7. Reduce. Ask your parents to start a compost pile in your backyard to reduce garbage. Fruits, vegetables, scrapes, and peelings can all be used to fertilize your garden.

Respect Planet Earth and Slow Down Climate Change

Problem: The increase in the Earth's temperature is causing lots of problems for the environment. Planet Earth gives us everything we need to live a happy life. We need to show planet Earth that we are grateful for all that we have!

8. Trees. Ask your parents or school to plant trees. Trees and plants eat up bad gases. The more trees we have, the cleaner the air.

9. Spend Time in Nature. Instead of watching T.V. or playing indoors, enjoy the fresh air outside and our beautiful planet.

10. Tell a Friend. Share this list with a friend. Everyone can make a difference!

Resources

(K= for Kids; P= for Parents; T= for Teachers)

Websites

Author's for Earth Day – These children's book authors visit schools and empower kids by donating to help Earth charities, chosen by students. https://www.rootsandshoots.org/ **K, T**

Balloons Blow – This organization educates learners about plastic pollution and encourages people *not* to do balloon release. https://balloonsblow.org/ **K, P, T**

Children of the Earth – Promotes a greater understanding and respect for animals, plants, water, soil, air and energy systems. Helps children comprehend the positive and negative environmental effects of our actions. http://www.childrenoftheearth.org/ **K, P, T**

Children of the Seventh Fire – Shows what other students are doing to protect and restore the environment in their communities and create peace. www.childrenoftheseventhfire.com/ **K, T**

Environmental Education for Kids – EEK! An online magazine for grades 4-8; contains articles and activities about animals, plants, and environmental issues. http://dnr.wi.gov/eek/ **K, T**

EPA: Water Sense Kids – Explores water saving tips for kids at Water Sense! An EPA partnership program. http://www.epa.gov/WaterSense/kids/simpleways.html **K, T**

Gardening for Beginners – Multiple ways for kids to learn about growing plants and caring for their environment. http://www.the10thcircle.com/gardening-for-beginners/ **K, P, T**

International Crane Foundation – Works worldwide to conserve cranes and their wetland habitats. https://www.savingcranes.org/ **K, P, T**

Jane Goodall's Roots & Shoots – This organization, part of the Jane Goodall Institute, is focused on helping young people create and carry out Earth-helping actions. https://www.rootsandshoots.org/ **K, P, T**

Kids for Saving the Earth – Provides an environmental curriculum for all ages that inspires, educates, and empowers children to protect the Earth. www.kidsforsavingearth.org. **K, P, T**

NASA's Climate Kids – Know your world, keep up with the latest, make stuff, play games, watch videos, and dream! http://climatekids.nasa.gov/ **K, T**

National Arbor Day – Provides information and resources about planting and caring for trees. www.arborday.org/ **K, P, T**

National Wildlife Federation – Publishes Ranger Rick and Ranger Rick Jr. They have a wildlife gardening program, a butterfly heroes program, and an eco-schools program. https://www.nwf.org/ **P, T**

Nature Challenge for Kids – The David Suzuki Foundation website starts with 10 simple ways to protect nature, followed by four challenge activities that offer first-hand experience with the natural world. www.davidsuzuki.org/what-you-can-do/ **K, P, T**

Sea Turtle Conservancy – This organization has kid-friendly programs to protect and monitor sea turtle nesting beaches. https://conserveturtles.org/ **K, P, T**

Three Sisters Garden – Provides instruction for planting a Three Sisters Garden. www.kidsgardening.com **K, P, T**

University of Minnesota: An Ojibway Arts in Education Model Program – Combines Ojibway arts and culture with a standard-based curriculum. www.intersectingart.umn.edu **P, T**

For Parents and Teachers:

Alliance For the Great Lakes – www.greatlakes.org
Clean Water Action Michigan – www.cleanwateraction.org/mi
Great Lakes Echo – www.greatlakesecho.org
Great Lakes Restoration Initiative – www.greatlakesrestoration.us/
U.S. Environmental Protection Agency (EPA) – www.epa.gov/

Books

Benton-Banai, Edward. *The Mishomis Book: The Voice of the Ojibway.* Hayward: Indian Country Communications, 1998.

Cornell, George L. and Gordon Henry Jr. *North American Indians Today*: Ojibway. Philadelphia: Madison Crest Publishers, 2004.

De Coteau Orie, Sandra. *Did You Hear the Wind Sing Your Name?* NY: Walker and Co., 1995.

Erdrich, Louise. *The Birchbark House.* New York: Hyperion Books for Children, 1999.

Gonzalez, Xelena. *All Around Us.* El Paso, Texas: Cinco Puntos Press, 2017.

Hart, Lisa. *Children of the Seventh Fire: An Ancient Prophecy for Modern Times.* Granville: The McDonald & Woodward Publishing Company, 2011.

Hamanaka, Sheila. *All the Colors of the Earth.* New York: Junior Books, 1994.

Kondonassis, Yolanda. *Our House is Round: A Kid's Book about Why Protecting Our Earth Matters.* New York: Skypony Press, 2012.

Rendon, Marcie R. *Powwow Summer: A Family Celebrates the Circle of Life.* Minneapolis, MN: Carolhoda Books, Inc., 1996.

Robertson, Joanne. *The Water Walker.* Toronto: Second Story Press, 2017.

Rohmer, Harriet. *Heroes of the Environment.* San Francisco, California: Chronicle Books, 2009.

Shilling, Vincent. *Native Defenders of the Environment.* TN: Green Press Initiative, 2011.

Smith, Cynthia, Leith. *Jingle Dancer.* New York: Morrow Junior Books, 2000.

Waboose, Jan Bourdeau. *Sky Sisters.* Toronto: Kids Can Press, 2000.

Cross-Curriculum Activities:
Literacy, Diversity, Friendship

Children of Native America Today by Yvonne Wakim. There are 500 Native nations and culture groups living in the United States today and each group has its own special heritage and cultural practices. In contrast to the perpetual myths of Native people from the past, these color photographs and descriptions provide the reader with contemporary information of the daily life of Native people today.

Extension: Discuss the phrase, *"Walk a Mile in My Shoes"* with students. How does this apply to the Native Water Walkers? What would it be like to walk in their shoes? Have students write a story about a day in their life—from their shoe's point of view. Children trace and cut out the outline of their shoe. Decorate and attach it to the writing piece titled: "Walk a Mile in My Shoes." Share stories and display on a bulletin board. Encourage children to write original poetry in Haiku or couplet form. Decorate a real shoe or a shoe pattern to display as a sign of either walking in peace or walking for the water.

Extension – Using the resources at the back of *Children of Native America Today,* have students explore websites, learn new vocabulary, or map out Native groups on a map of the United States (see pp 6-7). Divide students into cooperative groups and assign students research on each group by regional location (there are 9 when including Hawaii). Compare and contrast the various Native Nations using Venn diagrams, posters, slide presentations, etc. Make ABC books of the different Native cultures.

Crossing Bok Chitto by Tim Tingle. This is a story about a girl and boy who forge a friendship during a time when it was dangerous to be friends or even be together. Long before the Underground Railroad, the Choctaws were helping slaves escape and making them a part of their communities and families. *Crossing Bok Chitto* is a story about friendship, acceptance, and diversity.

Extension: Ask students to share stories about their family history. Are there events in their life, or in their family that they would like to preserve? Was there a time when they helped someone else? If so, what did they know about them? Why did they help them?

Giving Thanks: A Native American Good Morning Message by Chief Jake Swamp. *Giving Thanks* is a special children's version of the Thanksgiving Address—a message of gratitude that originated with the Native people of upstate New York and Canada. This Native message is based on the belief that the natural world is a gift and is precious. It is a celebration of the beauty of Mother Earth—from the moon and stars to the tiniest blade of grass.

Extension: As a class, read the story aloud. What are the gifts of life that are mentioned in the book? What are some things that keep the environment healthy? That damage it? Write about what kind of environment students would like to live in? Read haiku poems about nature. Have students write their own. Listen to the music of "Flight of the Bumblebee" that takes place in nature. Draw or use it as writing prompt for student's creative expression. Research the League of the Iroquois and their influence on the Founding Fathers of the United States.

Grandmother's Dreamcatcher by Becky Ray McCain. A Chippewa grandmother explains to her granddaughter, the legend of the dreamcatcher and the power it holds.

Extension – See instructions for making a dreamcatcher in this book. For a simple design see: http://www.pbs.org/parents/crafts-for-kids/dream-catcher/

I Am Earth: An Earth Day Book for Kids by James and Rebecca McDonald. A beginner's introduction to the concepts of earth science and environmental awareness, plus ways to keep Earth healthy and happy.

Extension: Compare and Contrast: Mother Earth Water walks with one listed on the following site. Create a Venn diagram or maps of the two differing water walks and the Native tribes that participate. http://www.nibiwalk.org/

Our Big Home: An Earth Poem by Linda Glaser. The book is a big thank-you note to the earth. It is a poem about the connections between people, plants, animals and the earth. The goal of the book is to lead children toward the all-important understanding of caring for the environment.

Extension: The earth does not have an address to receive thank-you notes. But writing thank-you notes and sharing words and art with others, can remind us about what nature does for us. Speak, write, photograph—draw, create posters, videos, essays, and other things to share what you have learned. Display your work or send your notes and art to newspapers, magazines, television stations, companies, and elected officials. Check out websites listed in this book for ways to take action. Discuss volunteerism. Ask students ways they can be responsible for caring for the earth. Ask students why they think the words in the story were placed in a circle? Write a short poem about earth gifts and place it on a circle pattern.

Stick and Stone by Beth Ferry. Best friends Stick and Stone have opportunities to help each other in a funny story of kindness along with a light anti-bullying message.

Discuss bullying and list ways how they can help reduce bullying amongst their peers. Write journal entries about their experiences.

Extension: Make Friendship bracelets (relates to the "tying of knots of friendship and threads of community"). Check out these sites: https://www.youtube.com/watch?v=n2rq-btMNFI https://www.instructables.com/id/how-to-make-a-friendship-bracelet-1/

Sometimes I Feel Like A Fox by Danielle Daniel. A playful introduction to the Anishinabek tradition of totem animals, the importance of totem animals in Native American culture, and how animal guides can help children understand themselves and others.

Extension: – Children can make animal masks from paper plates and construction paper to represent their own totem animal. Directions of YouTube - https://www.youtube.com/watch?v=jBsfcQwJDsQ Please read pp 18 - 26 of ***Lessons from Turtle Island,*** by Guy W. Jones. The authors describe topics of "Cultural Insensitivity".

Thank You Earth: A Love Letter to our Planet by April Sayre. This book is a photographic, panoramic view of the planet with writing concepts that highlight nature, geography, biology, and most importantly respect and gratitude for the many gifts that planet Earth gives us.

Extension*:* Have students write their own version of a love letter to the Earth or write thank you notes to others in their school or family. Students might like to illustrate their own thank-you page similar to a favorite page from the book. In addition there are a number of cultures and communities across the world that have traditions of thanking and celebrating the planet during certain seasons and holidays. Have students research some of these events.

English Language Arts Standards
Reading Informational Text

Grade 3	
CCSS.ELA-Literacy.RI.3.1	Ask and answer questions to demonstrate understanding of a text, referring explicitly to the text as the basis for the answers.
CCSS.ELA-Literacy.RI.3.3	Describe the relationship between a series of historical events, scientific ideas or concepts, or steps in technical procedures in a text, using language that pertains to time, sequence, and cause/effect.
CCSS.ELA-Literacy.RI.3.7	Use information gained from illustrations (e.g., maps, photographs) and the words in a text to demonstrate understanding of the text (e.g., where, when, why, and how key events occur).
CCSS.ELA-Literacy.RI.3.10	By the end of the year, read and comprehend informational texts, including history/social studies, science, and technical texts, at the high end of the grades 2-3 text complexity band independently and proficiently.
Grade 4	
CCSS.ELA-Literacy.RI.4.1	Refer to details and examples in a text when explaining what the text says explicitly and when drawing inferences from the text.
CCSS.ELA-Literacy.RI.4.3	Explain events, procedures, ideas, or concepts in a historical, scientific, or technical text, including what happened and why, based on specific information in the text.
CCSS.ELA-Literacy.RI.4.10	By the end of year, read and comprehend informational texts, including history/social studies, science, and technical texts, in the grades 4-5 text complexity band proficiently, with scaffolding as needed at the high end of the range.

English Language Arts Standards
Reading Literature

Grade 3	
CCSS.ELA-Literacy. RL.3.2	Recount stories, including fables, folktales, and myths from diverse cultures; determine the central message, lesson, or moral and explain how it is conveyed through key details in the text.
CCSS.ELA-Literacy. RL.3.3	Describe characters in a story (e.g., their traits, motivations, or feelings) and explain how their actions contribute to the sequence of events.
CCSS.ELA-Literacy. RL.3.7	Explain how specific aspects of a text's illustrations contribute to what is conveyed by the words in a story (e.g., create mood, emphasize aspects of a character or setting).
CCSS.ELA-Literacy. RL.3.10	By the end of the year, read and comprehend literature, including stories, dramas, and poetry, at the high end of the grades 2-3 text complexity band independently and proficiently.
Grade 4	
CCSS.ELA-Literacy. RL.4.3	Describe in depth a character, setting, or event in a story or drama, drawing on specific details in the text (e.g., a character's thoughts, words, or actions).
CCSS.ELA-Literacy. RL.4.9	Compare and contrast the treatment of similar themes and topics (e.g., opposition of good and evil) and patterns of events (e.g., the quest) in stories, myths, and traditional literature from different cultures.
Source: http://www.corestandards.org/	

Lake Huron Water Walk 2005

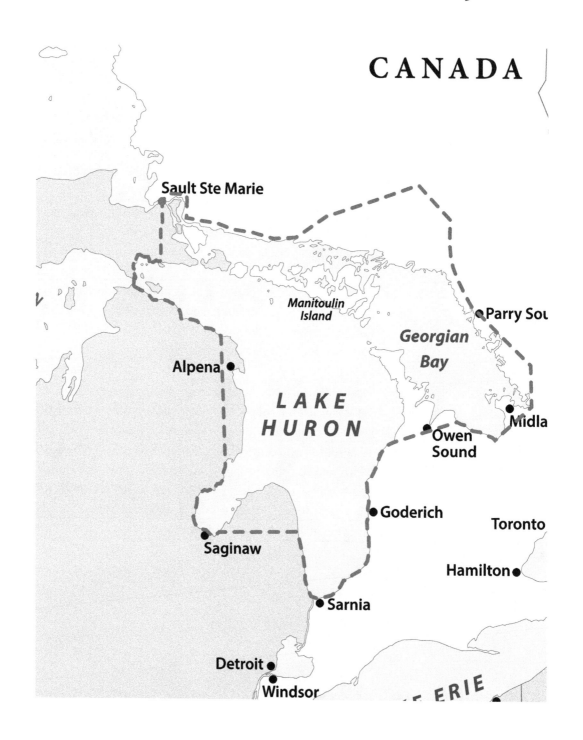

About the Artist—David W. Craig

David W. Craig

BORN AND RAISED IN THE state of Washington, David W. Craig grew up surrounded by land as alive as it is beautiful. David began private art lessons at the age of nine. After high school graduation, he pursued his life-long passion and earned a degree in art from Seattle Art Institute.

David has done freelance work for national parks and for various commercial organizations, but currently he focuses full time on his own style of painting. Weaving together story, emotion and moments in time with color and a vibrant sensitivity, each of David's pieces speaks to its viewers in a unique and powerful way. Watercolor mixed media, sculpturing, and leather work are some of his mediums.

Family ties are strong in the foothills of Mount "Rainer where David Craig paints and raises his two young daughters on a rural farm. Enrolled Chippewa (Ojibway), David and his daughters travel throughout the western United States attending tribal gatherings powwows and art shows.

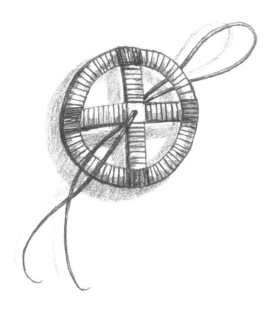

About the Author —Carol Trembath

BORN AND RAISED IN THE Great Lakes State of Michigan, Carol Trembath has made water a lifelong focus and passion. Her other interest is education. Carol has been a teacher, librarian, and media specialist for over 30 years. She earned a Masters Degree in Library and Information Science from Wayne State University and a Masters in Educational Technology from Michigan State University. However, her initial degree was in English from Western Michigan University and her "first love" is literature.

Ripples and Waves is the third book in the Water Walker series which presents what Native people are doing to protect the Great Lakes, rivers, and waterways across the United States and Canada. Carol's hope is that readers of her books: *Water Walkers* (Lake Superior), *Stepping*

Author Carol Trembath (right)
with Josephine Mandamin

Stones (Lake Michigan), and *Ripples and Waves* (Lake Huron), will become more aware of Native teachings and become involved in recycling and protecting the environment.

Carol's books have won the Eric Hoffer "eye of daVinci" award for their art work and a bronze medal in the category of multicultural at the Traverse City Moonbeam Awards. Carol has plans for more children's books that will continue Mai's journey to all of the Great Lakes. Her books can now be seen in three of Michigan's National Parks.

"Water," she said, "is our friend; and if you love something, you take care of it."
Visit her website at: CarolTrembath.com

CPSIA information can be obtained
at www.ICGtesting.com
Printed in the USA
BVHW060320200519
548308BV00001B/1/P

9 780990 744665